ROBERTO CLEMENTE

ROBERTO CLEMENTE

by Kenneth Rudeen

illustrated by Frank Mullins

THOMAS Y. CROWELL COMPANY   NEW YORK

CROWELL BIOGRAPHIES
Edited by Susan Bartlett Weber

Library of Congress Cataloging in Publication Data Rudeen, Kenneth. Roberto Clemente. (A Crowell biography) SUMMARY: A biography of Puerto Rico's Baseball hero, Roberto Clemente, the Pittsburgh Pirate who lost his life performing a final act of generosity. 1. Clemente, Roberto, 1934-1972—Juv. lit. [1. Clemente, Roberto, 1934-1972. 2. Baseball—Biography] I. Mullins, Frank, illus. II. Title. GV865.C45R82 1973 796.357'092'4 [B] [92] 73-12794 ISBN 0-690-00315-3 ISBN 0-690-00322-6 (lib. bdg.)

2   3   4   5   6   7   8   9   10

ROBERTO CLEMENTE

A CROWELL
BIOGRAPHY

When Roberto Clemente was a small boy in
Puerto Rico—long before he ever dreamed of
becoming a great baseball player—just having
a baseball was important. Not many boys had
real baseballs, white and round and firm with
neat stitches along the seams. Roberto and his
friends made their own baseballs. They would
find an old golf ball. That would be the center.
Then they would get some string and wind and
wind it around the golf ball and tape it all
together.

Roberto usually took the string from the tops of the bags that rice and beans came in. Every Puerto Rican family ate rice and beans. But there never seemed to be enough string. Roberto's mother would find him in the kitchen and say, "Oh, *Mome,* not again."

Mome was Roberto's nickname. When his mother and father and brothers and sisters said it, it sounded like Mo-may. "Mo-may," Mrs. Clemente would say, "I wish you would not take the string out of the bags."

And Roberto would say, "But I have to have a baseball, Mama."

In Puerto Rico baseball was the favorite sport. Baseball players were heroes to Roberto.

Puerto Rico is one of the islands that stretch out like steppingstones from the southern tip of Florida into the warm, blue sea. The island is beautiful, but for most of the people life is hard. In the sky the sun shines brightly. Foamy waves splash against the shore. Green mountains rise up from the sea. Birds with gaily colored feathers sing in the trees.

But men are not free to fly like birds. They must work long hours in the cities or in the fields. To be a baseball player is to be like a bird. That is a way to fly up from the hard life.

Roberto Clemente was born in the town of Carolina on August 18, 1934. The town is nestled in a valley not far from the big city of San Juan. When Roberto was growing up, there were large fields of sugar cane all around Carolina. They looked a little like the cornfields of the United States. The canes were slender and tall, growing to a height well above a man's head. They had sharp, narrow leaves that cut like a razor if you brushed against one by mistake.

To Roberto and his friends the sugar cane

was like candy. They would peel back the bark on a piece of cane and bite and suck on the chewy pulp inside to get its sweet taste.

Roberto knew the fields especially well. His father was a foreman for a big sugar cane company. He saw that other workers in the fields did their jobs properly.

A man did not get rich working in the cane fields. An ordinary worker received only $2 a day. A foreman like Roberto's father received $3 or $4 a day.

In Roberto's family there was no money for luxuries like new baseballs. But there was always enough rice and beans and chicken and pork on the table. Roberto's small house, which was made of wood and had a zinc roof, stood near a grove of bamboo trees.

Roberto's father was strict. When he gave his sons jobs to do, they did them. One day he asked Roberto and another son to move a large pile of sand. It was hard work to shovel the heavy sand, and the sun was hot.

"Roberto, I feel sick," his brother said.

Roberto looked at his brother. Sweat stood out on his forehead and his face was pale.

"Go on home," Roberto said. "I will finish the job."

It was easy to say, but when his brother was gone, Roberto had to face the pile of sand all by himself. It looked so high he wanted to give up. But he didn't.

Roberto worked harder than he ever had before. When he was finished at last, he ran for home, because his father had told him not to be late for dinner. He was tired and he ached, but inside he felt good.

From Monday to Friday, Roberto went to school. Often his thoughts were tugged from his books by the warm sun and gentle breezes outside the classroom window—tugged to the ball park, where someday he hoped to play.

In the meantime he had to be content, after school, with balls made of string and tape and games played in a rough clearing that was not even level.

There were other boys much better at baseball than Roberto. People did not say, "Roberto is going to be a great ballplayer." He was small and thin. He could not hit the ball as hard or throw it as far as the bigger boys of his age.

Roberto and his friends played a game that was more like softball than baseball. They did not have the gloves or catching masks and pads to handle the hard, stinging baseball that the big-leaguers use.

But they saw the real game played in the park in Carolina—and they longed to play there, too, someday.

While he loved baseball and played as much as he could on the field the boys used, after school Roberto always ran first to the sugar cane fields. There he met his father and rode home with him on his horse. Papa Clemente climbed into the saddle and Roberto scrambled up behind him. Then off they rode to the house with the bamboo trees.

One day, when Roberto was nine years old, he was late. Papa Clemente rode off without him. A car came along and crashed into the horse. Papa Clemente was thrown. He was badly hurt and had to spend two months in a hospital.

"It is a miracle Roberto was spared," his father said. "If he had been riding with me as

usual, I am afraid he would have been killed."

When time came for Roberto to go to high school, he was happy. The high school had a real baseball field. It had real baseballs, gloves, and masks.

Roberto played in the outfield. He had to run fast to get to balls that were hit in his direction and throw hard to keep the hitter from running to extra bases.

Roberto had always been a fast runner. Now he worked hard to become a good thrower and a good hitter. Roberto's high school had a track team. Besides running on the team, Roberto also threw the javelin, which is like a spear. When you throw it, the javelin sails through the air and then comes down and sticks in the ground.

Roberto threw the javelin to make his arm strong for baseball. In time he became one of the best throwers on his baseball team.

In high school Roberto was a quiet and serious boy. "He did not want to be just an

ordinary person, he wanted to be the best," one of his friends says.

Just before Roberto was graduated from high school he was chosen to play for the team in Santurce. Santurce is a town near Carolina. Roberto was paid to play baseball for this town. He did not make a great deal of money, but it was more than anyone in the sugar fields could make.

Even better, now Roberto was *somebody.* People turned their heads to look at him when he walked in the plaza. To his old friends he was still *Mome,* but to everybody else he was the new young ballplayer, Roberto Clemente.

It was a name soon to be heard in the United States, where the best players in baseball perform in two major leagues. They are called the National League and the American League.

Roberto wanted to be the best. He wanted to play in the major leagues. Men who look for new players for the major leagues came to see him in Puerto Rico. They saw him hit the ball hard. They saw him catch it in the outfield with sure hands. They saw him throw the ball fast and true. They saw him run swiftly.

In 1954, when Roberto was nineteen years old, he was chosen by one of the most famous teams in the National League, the Brooklyn Dodgers.

He was very happy to have this chance. The Dodgers were the team of Jackie Robinson. Jackie was the first black man to play in the major leagues. He was a wonderful player, but he had many problems with white people who did not accept black men as equals.

Like Robinson, Roberto Clemente was black. But while growing up in Puerto Rico, he did not think about the color of a person's

skin. Black men and men with light skin had always played baseball together in Puerto Rico.

So while Roberto was happy, he was also scared. He was going far from home for the first time in his life, and to places where black men still were not always treated fairly.

First Roberto was sent to Montreal in Canada to play for a farm team of the Dodgers. A farm team helps prepare young players for the major leagues.

Roberto probably was good enough to be on the Dodgers. But this was still a time when there were not very many black men in the major leagues. Some people said that the major leagues did not want to have more than four black players on any one team.

The Brooklyn Dodgers already had four black players. That was one of the reasons,

people said, why Roberto was sent to the
Montreal farm team.

But now the Dodgers had a problem. They
wanted to keep Roberto for the future, but by
sending him to a farm team just then they ran
the risk of losing him. Scouts for other teams
might discover him. One of these teams might
take him.

The Dodgers did not want that to happen.
They wanted to hide Roberto from these
scouts. But how were they to do it? The
Dodgers could not put him in a cave, or a

closet. They had to try to hide him right out in the open as he played baseball for Montreal. They tried to do this by making it look as if Roberto were not as good a player as he really was.

It was not easy to hide Roberto. The manager of the Montreal team did his best. When Roberto was doing fine in a game, the manager would take him out. When Roberto was having just an ordinary day, the manager would leave him in.

Roberto did not know why he was being

treated this way. He became confused and angry. He was lonely, anyway, living among strangers so far from home. He had grown up speaking Spanish. The people on his team spoke English, and the people in Montreal mostly spoke French.

There were trips to other cities to play other farm teams, so there were new sights for Roberto to see and new people to meet. He had money to spend. He had a good-looking uniform, and he had time to practice batting and throwing and running.

Roberto might have enjoyed all these things, but life seemed upside-down. The better he played, the quicker he was taken from a game. The worse he played, the longer he stayed in. At times he thought about quitting baseball and going home to Puerto Rico.

But his desire to play, and to be the best, was stronger than his loneliness and his anger. He kept on playing.

The Dodgers just could not make him look bad enough. Other teams could see that he was a fine player. Scouts for the Pittsburgh Pirates, another team in the National League, watched Roberto closely. They decided to take him and have him play for them.

Pittsburgh is not a place of tall sugar cane fields and gaily colored birds. It is a big, smoky city. But its people do have one thing in common with the people of Carolina, Puerto Rico. They love their baseball team.

Right from the start they loved Roberto. He was tremendous as a fielder. He had a trick of catching a ball way up in the air, with both of his feet off the ground, and then whirling to throw the ball back to the infield before his feet came down to earth. He thought nothing of crashing into walls and fences if he had to do that to catch a ball.

He became an excellent hitter. In baseball a really good hitter is one who gets three hits in every ten chances at bat. If he does that, he is said to be batting three hundred. In his second year with Pittsburgh, Roberto was batting better than three hundred.

More and more black men, more and more Spanish-speaking players like Roberto were coming into major league baseball. Soon there was no more talk of keeping the number of black players on a team down to four.

But still there were times when Roberto felt that he and other Spanish-speaking players were treated unfairly. He believed that they were not given as much praise and publicity as the others, even when they were just as good. Roberto was the kind of man who could make people listen to him. He asked for equal treatment for Spanish-speaking players. Whenever he could help one of them, he did.

Once the regular Pittsburgh shortstop could not play. A Spanish-speaking player was put in his place. This player was new to the team and nervous. He made some mistakes. Other players on the team were angry with him.

Roberto found him later, crying in the dressing room. "You are coming to dinner with me tonight," Roberto said. At dinner Roberto cheered him up. Then he asked the other Pirates to be more patient with the

shortstop. They were, and he played well in
some very important games.

By 1960 Roberto's Pirates were strong
enough to win the championship of the National League. They played the American
League champions, the New York Yankees, in
the World Series. There were seven games in
that World Series. Roberto made a hit in every
game and the Pirates won.

Roberto was getting better and better as a player, but he was not always happy. Often he was sick or injured. Playing as hard as he did, he would tear muscles. Once he had malaria, an illness of chills and fevers.

Even so, Roberto went on to win four batting championships in the National League. Nearly every year he was a member of the All-Star team—the best players from all the teams in the National League.

Every winter, after the major league base-ball season ended in the United States, Roberto went home to Puerto Rico. Once when he was in Carolina he met one of his old high school teachers in a drugstore. As he was talking to her, a lovely girl walked past.

"Do you know her?" Roberto asked his friend, the teacher.

"Yes, I do," the teacher said. "That is Vera Zabala."

"Will you introduce me?" Roberto asked.

That is how Roberto met the woman he married. They built a beautiful house in the town of Rio Piedras, which is near Carolina, and in time they had three little boys.

The basement of the house in Rio Piedras was Roberto's workshop. As a child he had liked to make things of clay. He had shaped small figures of people and animals and let them bake in the Carolina sun until they were

hard. Now in Rio Piedras he took clay and made it into baseball gloves and bats.

When Roberto talked to young Puerto Ricans, he remembered the rough playing field of his boyhood and he began to dream of a sports city for the island. There young people would be able to play baseball, basketball, tennis, and soccer with the best equipment.

Each spring he returned to the United States to play for the Pirates. But not until 1971 did he and the Pirates win another National

League championship and go into another World Series.

Now the Pirates faced the Baltimore Orioles. Nearly everybody thought Baltimore was a better team than Pittsburgh, and the Orioles won the first game easily. The next day they won again. Those games were played in Baltimore on the Orioles' home field. It is often easier to win at home than on the opponent's field.

There were to be three games in Pittsburgh. To the great joy of that city, the Pirates won all three games. To win a World Series one team must win four games. So now the Pirates needed just one more victory. But the next game would be played in Baltimore.

Baltimore won that game by the close score of 3 to 2. The winners of the next game would be the world champions. And again the game would be played in Baltimore.

The stadium in Baltimore was packed with cheering fans. Millions of people were watching the game on television.

The score was zero to zero when Roberto stepped up to bat in the fourth inning. He made a twisting motion with his head to relieve the pain he had been feeling all week in his neck. He looked out at the Baltimore pitcher, Mike Cuellar.

Cuellar was a man who threw slow, tricky pitches that were difficult to hit. He threw. The ball floated in toward Roberto. Crack! went the bat. The ball flew over the outfield and into the seats beyond. It was a home run. Pittsburgh was ahead in the game, 1 to 0.

In the eighth inning the Pirates scored another run. Baltimore scored a run in the eighth inning, too, but the Orioles could do nothing after that to draw even. The game ended. The Pirates had won the Series in the last possible

game by the score of 2 to 1. Without Roberto's home run, who knows what might have
happened?

Just as he had in 1960, Roberto made a hit in
every game of the World Series. He was voted
the most valuable player of the Series by the
reporters who wrote about it. Of all the players on both teams, Roberto Clemente was the
very best.

He went home to a hero's welcome in Puerto Rico. A huge crowd was at the airport in San Juan to meet his plane. The governor of the island presented him with a gold medal.

There was just one more thing left in baseball for Roberto to do. That was to make 3,000 hits. He would soon be thirty-eight years old—very old for a ballplayer. Only ten men in the entire history of baseball had ever played long enough or well enough to make 3,000 hits. These were special heroes.

At the very end of the 1972 season, on September 30 in Pittsburgh, Roberto hit Number 3,000.

Roberto went home to his family in Rio Piedras. He wanted to rest and also to plan for the sports city for the boys and girls of Puerto Rico.

In December he heard terrible news. In the city of Managua in the Central American

country of Nicaragua there had been an earthquake. The ground trembled and shook be-
neath the city. Buildings cracked and fell.
Fires broke out. More than 10,000 people
were killed. More than 200,000 people lost
their homes.

Around the world people began sending money and food and medicine and clothing to help the earthquake victims. Roberto asked the many Puerto Ricans he knew to help out as much as they could. He did more.

On December 31 he climbed aboard a plane loaded with supplies to take them to the people of Managua. The plane, heavily laden, rose slowly from the San Juan airport and headed out to sea. Then, when it was just a mile away, it plunged into the ocean.

That night was New Year's Eve, usually a time of gaiety and celebration, but there was no gaiety in Puerto Rico. Thousands of people went to the beach to look for the wreckage of the plane. When it became clear that Roberto had drowned, Puerto Ricans and many people in the United States felt sad. A great player—and man—was gone.

In the United States Roberto was elected to

baseball's Hall of Fame. This is the greatest honor a baseball player can receive. The Hall of Fame building is in Cooperstown, New York. In it there are pictures of the best players, and things like their bats and caps.

A sign was placed on the door of the room Roberto had lived in during spring training with the Pirates in Florida. It read, "I want to be remembered as a ballplayer who gave all he had to give."

It was signed,
"Roberto Clemente."

ABOUT THE AUTHOR

While he was still in high school, Ken Rudeen started his career in journalism by stuffing Sunday newspaper sections in the mail-room of the *Kansas City Star.* Eventually he became a copy boy and then, at seventeen, a reporter. Later he studied at the University of Kansas and served as the *Star's* campus correspondent.

Mr. Rudeen lives in South Salem, New York, with his wife and their daughter Louisa. He has written several books as well as numerous newspaper and magazine articles. Now he works as an editor for *Sports Illustrated* magazine.

ABOUT THE ILLUSTRATOR

Frank Mullins' portraits have been used on more than a dozen covers of *Sports Illustrated* magazine and in numerous other publications. This well-known free-lance artist is a graduate of Pratt Institute and of Teachers College, Columbia University. His work has appeared in many exhibitions and is included in the collections of the United States Air Force, American Chemical Society, and Northwestern University as well as in many private collections.

Mr. Mullins, his wife, and their three children live in Sharon, Connecticut. He teaches there at the Sharon Creative Arts Foundation and at Pratt Institute in Brooklyn, New York.